METHU

The aim of t...
Different volumes present material wri

from the expanding repertoire now bei
playwrights and a variety of youth thea..... ...., ...
professional and amateur. Each play is prefaced by an account of the
original conception and performance and suggestions are given for future
presentation.

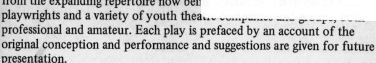

TIMESNEEZE is a science-fiction fantasy written for performance by a small
cast of adults and a large number of children. As the sneeze-prone hero,
Basher, whirls through the ages to encounter Arthurian legend, Arabian
nights, the Betweentimers and the Machine people, the audience can be
brought in when and where the director wishes. As David Campton explains
in his Introduction, the script is infinitely flexible, a point which was proved
by the first presentation of the play by the National Theatre Company
under the direction of Roland Joffe at the Jeanetta Cochrane Theatre in
1970. He describes the methods used at that time to involve young audiences
and suggests a few more which will certainly help companies and schools to
bring *Timesneeze* to uproarious life wherever it is performed.

... plays for children by
contemporary writers
(**The Cutting of Marchan Wood**
by Richard M Hughes;
The Boy Without a Head
by Edward Lucie-Smith;
Tamburlane the Mad Hen
by Adrian Mitchell;
**The Legend of Scarface and Blue
Water**
by Niki Marvin)
for 8–14 year-olds

JOHN FORD'S CUBAN MISSILE CRISIS
a play put together collectively by
the Bradford Art College Theatre
Group
edited and introduced by Albert
Hunt
for 15 year-olds upwards

THE ADVENTURES OF GERVASE BECKET
or The Man Who Changed Places
a play by Peter Terson
originally written for the Victoria
Theatre, Stoke-on-Trent
edited and introduced by Peter
Cheeseman
for 8–14 year-olds

SNAP OUT OF IT
a programme about mental illness
devised by the Leeds Playhouse
Theatre-in-Education Team
edited by Roger Chapman and
Brian Wilks
with an Introduction by Brian
Wilks
for 15 year-olds upwards

INCREDIBLE VANISHING!!!!
a play by Denise Coffey
originally written for the
Young Vic Theatre Company
for 8–12 year-olds

OLD KING COLE
a play by Ken Campbell
originally written for the Victoria
Theatre, Stoke-on-Trent
for 8–12 year-olds

SCHOOL FOR CLOWNS
a play by F. K. Waechter
translated by Ken Campbell
commissioned and first
staged by the Unicorn Theatre
for 7–12 year-olds and upwards

SWEETIE PIE
a play about women in society
devised by the Bolton Octagon
Theatre-in-Education Company
with an Introduction by Eileen
Murphy
for 14 year-olds upwards

PONGO PLAYS 1-6
six plays by Henry Livings
with music by Alex Glasgow
for 12 year-olds upwards

RARE EARTH
a programme about pollution
devised by the Belgrade Coventry
Theatre-in-Education Company
for 9–11 year-olds

TIME-SNEEZE

A Play by David Campton

Introduced by David Campton
With a Foreword by
Geoffrey Hodson

First published in Great Britain 1974
by Eyre Methuen Ltd
11 New Fetter Lane, London EC4P 4EE
Reprinted 1975 and 1978
Copyright © 1974 David Campton
Foreword ©1974 Geoffrey Hodson

Set by Expression Typesetters
Printed in Great Britain by
Fletcher & Sons Ltd, Norwich

ISBN 0 413 31410 3 (net)
ISBN 0 423 46940 1 (non-net)

Foreword

The original production of this script should have heralded a bright new world in professional young people's theatre in Great Britain. As there has been a delay in its publication we can now see it was a false dawn. Can we have another volunteer to push up the sun again please?

In 1970 the Arts Council of Great Britain had been handing out crisp new bank notes for three years to Regional Theatres adding young people's work to their brief; Frank Dunlop had persuaded his management to build an experimental theatre next to an old butcher's shop in The Cut and call it the Young Vic; most important of all Roland Joffe had joined this new theatre from Leicester.

Roland had several bright ideas:
1 young people's theatre needs a new kind of play and a new look at staging;
2 the author should still be very active during rehearsals and early performances;
3 the designer should still be very active during rehearsals and early performances;
4 actors need to get to know children, to like and trust them.

All these ideas were realized to some extent in the original production of this play. There are too many generalizations and pre-conceived notions about children - particularly from theatre folk. *Timesneeze* gave actors, a writer, designers, a director and technical staff first-hand knowledge of individual children - contemporary, real children.

I hope the publication of this enterprise inspires others to dare the professional mix of theatre and teaching. For me it is a prerequisite for all professional theatre people working with children and young people that they must get to know them personally.

Timesneeze was a living, human experience. More please.

Geoffrey Hodson
Senior Inspector of Drama
I.L.E.A.

Introduction

Any script is the blue-print from which the final production is constructed. This definition applies particularly to *Timesneeze*, with the addition that the blue-print can always be modified. In describing anything that happened in the original production, I am not suggesting that this should be repeated. I am merely pointing to one way in which the play was approached. There must be hundreds of others, and I hope they will be pursued.

The play was commissioned by the National Theatre for the first season of what was to become the Young Vic Company. The Young Vic Theatre was not at that time ready, and the performance took place at the Jeanetta Cochrane Theatre, which assumed a new look for the occasion. The production was in every way a collaboration. The words and situations are mine, but everyone in the theatre company had some effect on the finished product - director, designers, musicians all contributed something, and the script was changed to accommodate their ideas (when they were good ones). However, being forewarned, I made the first draft as flexible as possible.

Flexibility was the first demand. As the production was to be half-improvisation there had to be scope for last-minute alterations and on-the-spot adjustments. Paradoxically, this meant that the framework had to be very sound. To avoid the risk of a performance collapsing in chaos, the actors had to be confident that there were thoroughly rehearsed points in the action, to which they could turn if audience and extras (which were the same) got out of hand.

The idea presented to me by Roland Joffe, who directed, was of a play in which the main parts would be played by experienced actors, but with lots of small parts which could be improvised on the spot. The audience was to be divided into four groups, and the play was to be devised in four parts (with a prologue and epilogue to get everything launched and wound up). In each part a quarter of the audience would act while everyone else watched. So in *Timesneeze* a quarter of the audience were from King Arthur's time, a quarter from the Arabian Nights, a quarter Betweentimers and a quarter Machine People.

To make this physically possible, peripheral staging was used. That is to say, the scenery was set up all round the walls of the theatre. There were no seats, and the audience grouped itself around the action wherever it was taking place, moving with the actors.

For some performances the audience/actors were told well in advance what their scene would be about. They were then able to decide what they were going to do and make quite elaborate costumes and properties. For some performances the audience/ actors were not told what was going to happen until they actually arrived at the theatre. Each performance worked in its own way. The forewarned actors had time to work on music and singing and dancing; while those to whom the idea was new gave fresh and spontaneous reactions to the situations.

Even when the audiences knew what the story-line was going to be, they were surprised by the setting, which had a magic of its own. The theatre was converted into a place that was half-factory, half-laboratory. A maze of pipes and tubes ran over the ceiling and around the walls. Here and there were boilers, drums and tanks, connected to the system of pipes. All these were brightly coloured as though made of plastics. As Basher made his way from period to period, so the scenery changed. When he was transported to King Arthur's Court, a large tank opened up to reveal the King sitting on a dais. As the tournament was about to begin, overhead pipes opened to let down banners. When Basher moved on to the Arabian Desert, palms grew up out of drums. For Betweentimers transparent plastic tubing lit up with tiny bulbs inside, giving the impression of a cascade of light. The Computer's mouth was made by two parallel pieces of pipe, which parted to reveal teeth. This changing scenery helped to direct the audience towards the action: when plastic tubing turns into a fountain the natural reaction is to go over to it to find out what is happening.

However, such splendidly complicated scenery, although adding gaiety to the original production, is not essential. The atmosphere of each period can be created by the properties brought on by the actors - banners and hobby-horses (broom handles with horses heads) for the tournament, camels in the caravan (two people under a length of hessian can be used to make a camel), and so on. The less scenery there is, the more notice audiences will take of properties and costumes.

The costume designers for the Jeanetta Cochrane production had some clever ideas, particularly the suggestion that the Black Knight should have three heads. In practice, three heads proved to be cumbersome, so they were reduced to three faces, but they added to the Knight's terrifying appearance. His armour, too, built him up into a lumbering menace. The Tinkerwoman was padded with several layers of foam plastic sewn into her dress. The Loper had built-up boots, a long robe, and a large bald dome on his head, making him tower over everyone else. The Machine Man had an electric light on top of his head. However, it is to be hoped that other designers will have ideas of their own. There is no reason why the Loper should not look like an undertaker, or even a wolf. One point to bear in mind is that, however fantastic the costumes worn by the leading characters may be, they must be easy to put on and take off, because the leading characters have some very quick changes. This is because Smith and Jones, the Tealady, H.E. and Miss E. play the people whom Basher meets on his travels. (It is a moot point whether they really exist, or whether Basher is imagining them.)

This doubling also means that Arthur, the Tinkerwoman, the Wazir, the Scorer, etc., should have traces in their characterization of the people in the Time Laboratory. However, all these characters have been drawn with the broadest possible strokes, so that the actors can fill in the details as they wish. For instance, King Arthur was originally conceived as an old man. The director was fascinated by the Emperor Franz Joseph of Austria and his Court, which was so hedged about with protocol, precedents, rules and procedures, that it was a wonder anyone managed to do anything, and he wanted Arthur to be that sort of person. The actor eventually cast as Arthur, though, was a young man. He argued that the only way for him to play an old man with the audience only a few inches away would be to make him into an unconvincing caricature. So Arthur was played as a young man - he was only sixteen anyway when he came to be King - almost pathetically idealistic, and so concerned about doing the right thing that he carried the Rules of Chivalry around with him everywhere; with almost the same results as Franz Joseph's rigid code of conduct. It is to be hoped that the actors playing the other parts will approach them in the same imaginative way. It can be seen that the Tinkerwoman is a fat, jolly, crook: but how did she come to be in the middle of the Arabian Nights? Work that one out.

The approach to the small parts will be somewhat different. There it is up to the actors to make up their minds what they want to be, and then stick to that. Almost any number of small parts can be created. For instance, there is no mention of Merlin in the Arthur scenes, but there is no reason why he should not appear. Early in rehearsals for the Young Vic production, someone had the idea of introducing a Court Painter. This character, it was assumed, would be dashing around making lightning sketches of the King; and Arthur would automatically freeze into postures from time to time, almost as though a photographer were telling him to 'hold it' - all this while talking to Basher about something quite different. The caravan to Bagdad will be made up of many different sorts of travellers, each with his own attitude to the Tinkerwoman. Part of the fun in this scene lies in the way the Tinkerwoman persuades them all to act in the same way for her benefit. The character, appearance and behaviour of the Betweentimers, since they belong to no place or period, can be left entirely to the imagination of the performers. There are perhaps fewer opportunities for individual characterization with the Machine People - until they start to sneeze and the spell is broken - but there is scope for linking actions; what one person does affecting his neighbour, making a machine-like pattern of movement.

The play has been deliberately constructed so that the crowds have their moments - the tournament, the auction, the surrounding of Basher by the Betweentimers, and the march of the Machine People - but other opportunities can be made. When schools took part in the original production, some classes complained that they did not have enough to do. So they put in interludes of their own - a mummers' play before the tournament began, and Eastern entertainers, including travelling players with a bloodthirsty melodrama, with the caravan, who started to perform the moment it stopped. The chances are there to be taken.

To give some guidance with the processional entrances and

exits, one of the experienced actors came in at the head of each crowd. Guinevere was at the head of the Arthurian Court; the Wazir showed the caravan the way; the Scorer looked after the Betweentimers; and the Machine Man brought in the Machine People.

Each of these entrances was accompanied by music and singing. Songs can be made up to suit the occasion, with very simple words and tunes. In the London production, the Court sang:

> 'Tournament Today,
> Tournament Today,
> There is going to be a
> Tournament Today.'

The Betweentimers sang 'Mangoldwurzel, Pretzelwurzel', the Machine People sang numbers, and the caravan sang 'Bagdad, Bagdad, we're going to - Bagdad''. The tunes all complimented each other (though there was no reason why the same tune should not have been used for all the songs); and at the end of the play, when everyone came into the Laboratory, everyone sang his or her song, and they all blended together. In fact, everyone came together in a long, long procession which wound its way all round the Laboratory and then out.

So music is needed. Music made in any sort of way, depending on the talent and performers available. For the Young Vic production, a very good percussionist came over from the National Theatre, and all the music was performed on percussion instruments (with the exception of a contraption like a musical saw that provided a grating accompaniment to the Loper's speech - but that was more sound effect than music). Live music is essential because with the free form of the script the musicians become part of the action. Although at times the actors follow the music, there are times when the music follows the actors - like the pantomime device in which the bass drum is whacked whenever a comedian falls down.

The actress playing the Tinkerwoman arrived at one rehearsal with a song which she had written herself to the tune of an Irish Jig. Of course, it went into the play. That is what the play is for. The script is only the beginning, and everyone - actors, producer, costume designers, scene painters, musicians, etc., etc., should add, and add, and add. If necessary, throw away the play we first thought of.

Timesneeze was first performed by the National Theatre Company at the Jeanetta Cochrane Theatre on 7 March 1970 with the following cast:

BASHER	Nicky Henson
SMITH	Barry James
JONES	Lionel Guyett
TEA LADY	Helen Burns
H.E.	Job Stewart
MISS E.	Kate Coleridge
KING ARTHUR	Barry James
THE BLACK KNIGHT	Lionel Guyett
GUINEVERE	Kate Coleridge
TINKERWOMAN	Helen Burns
WAZIR	Job Stewart
THE SCORER	Kate Coleridge
THE LOPER	Lionel Guyett
MACHINE PERSON	Barry James
COMPUTOR	Job Stewart

Directed by Roland Joffe

BASHER is working. He takes the Time Converter from under his bench, and begins to work on it. SMITH and JONES, two Laboratory Assistants, come up behind him.

SMITH: Basher!

(BASHER tries to cover up his work.)

JONES: There's no need to cover it up.

SMITH: You're wasting time again.

BASHER: No, I'm not - I - I . . . (Sneezes.)

SMITH: We know you by now, Basher. You're sneezing.

BASHER: I can't help it . . .

JONES: When you tell a lie, you sneeze. We know it. You know it.

BASHER: You're wrong. This is for the firm. I - hi - hi - (Sneezes.)

SMITH: You're a time-wasting liar. We've been through all this before. It's your fool of a Time Machine.

BASHER: It's not, it's . . .

JONES: Time Converter, then. (Reciting.) It doesn't move through time: it converts the time round it. Read your Einstein.

SMITH: It doesn't work. You just think you're clever. You just think the boss's daughter will fancy you if you're clever. In fact all the idiot thing does is waste your time, and ours.

BASHER: It would work. If only I had the time to . . .

JONES: In case you've forgotten, Basher - we are working on the Mark IV Project.

SMITH: Remember? It's what we're paid for.

JONES: And what are you doing?

SMITH: Where's the timing device for Miss E.?

BASHER: It's — almost finished.

JONES: Miss E. is waiting.

SMITH: So we're all waiting.

JONES: You know you're part of this research team, too.

SMITH: More's the pity.

JONES: Those productivity bonuses depend on results.

SMITH: You haven't got a flaming wife and family to support.

JONES: To say nothing of the mortgage rates going up. We need that money, and we're not losing it because of a time-wasting squirt like you.

SMITH: We'll just have to tell Miss E. the timing device isn't ready.

JONES: That'll make her happy. I've had enough of this. I'm going to H.E. himself. Let's see what he can do.

(As they go, BASHER puts the Time Converter away and works on a small device.)

BASHER: Time-wasting squirt! Perhaps you'd like me to lie down while you wipe your shoes on me. One of these days *I'll* start throwing my weight around. Respect. A person's entitled to a bit of respect. Even though he does nothing but fit timing devices together all day. Timing devices! (He is about to throw it across the room, but changes his mind.) I've got more brains in my little finger than . . . One of these days you're going to respect me.

(He realizes that he is making this last gesture of defiance at the TEA LADY, who has wheeled in her trolley.)

TEA LADY: Any time, Basher.

BASHER: Oh, it's you. (Taking it out on somebody.) And my name isn't Basher. It's Ba - ha - ha - ha . . . Shoo.

TEA LADY: I find Basher easier to say.

BASHER: To hell with this sneeze. Basher's sneezing. Basher's lying. It's murder. And I'm not lying. I'm . . . I'm . . .

TEA LADY: Are you sure? Who do you think you are? Think about it.

BASHER: I'm never going to get on while I've got a - ha - ha -

ha . . .

TEA LADY: Hay fever? I know a very good thing - only ten bob a bottle.

BASHER: Cup of tea.

TEA LADY: You owe me a week's tea money.

BASHER: Do I? No, I don't. You tried that on last week.

TEA LADY: Toss you double or quits.

BASHER: You're an old crook.

TEA LADY: I know. Isn't it wonderful? And I thrive on it, too. Like to buy a raffle ticket? Got your lucky number on it.

BASHER: What have you got to be so cheerful about?

TEA LADY: Them horrors getting on to you again? Come on. Have your tea.

BASHER: They've got it in for me. Just because I get ideas.

TEA LADY: Depends on your ideas. I've seen you giving Miss E. the eye.

BASHER: Her?

TEA LADY: Seen her looking you over, too.

BASHER: Me? The boss's daughter? You're joking. But you wait. She'll see. When she sees me in a Jag - sleek and new and shining. None of your worn-out jallopies. And Saville Row suits. You'll see the birds with their eyes popping out. Just you wait.

TEA LADY: I'll wait.

BASHER: I've got ideas I tell you. They'll make money.

TEA LADY: You tell the Boss. Here he is.

(H.E. sails in - outwardly icy, but inwardly seething.)

H.E.: Basher!

BASHER: Sir?

H.E.: I've just had a report from Smith and Jones. The project is behind schedule.

BASHER: Nearly ready now, sir.

H.E.: You do know what co-operation is, don't you? We work as a team here. One weak link and we all suffer. You — are — a — weak — link. (He finds himself shouting, and recovers himself.)

BASHER (muttering): Sorry, sir.

H.E.: I built this company up from a garage in Surbiton. I have watched it grow. It will grow more and more. We all benefit from a successful company. Bonuses. New washrooms. Bigger canteens. Greener playing fields. Higher pension schemes. I have seen this company grow, and I intend to see it grow further. We must become richer. More powerful. We must grow stronger than our competitors. You know that we have competitors?

BASHER: Yes, sir.

H.E.: Unscrupulous, evil men, whose only ambition is to see this company beaten into the ground. I know what they are doing. They are encroaching on our markets, stealing our customers. Our competitors must be wiped out. They are evil companies run by evil men. Infamous creatures, making vile products. They must be crushed, bankrupted, liquidated, taken over, wiped out, beaten into the ground. (He realizes that he is shouting again and pulls himself together.) As long as we understand each other.

BASHER: Yes, sir.

H.E.: Think of that when you're tempted to waste time.

BASHER: It isn't a waste of time, sir.

H.E.: Are you contradicting me?

BASHER: I've invented something, sir.

H.E.: I've heard about it. Time Converter you call it. I don't want to hear any more.

BASHER: No, sir. Not that. It's - it's a Millitignum Crystal Alternator.

H.E.(now brought up sharply): Millitignum? Have you been misappropriating millitignum? Do you realize that millitignum costs a thousand pounds an ounce?

BASHER: Only enough to cover a pin-head, sir. And it works. It really works. I've tested it on mice. They went mad and died - sir.

H.E.: It works, you said? Where is it?

BASHER: Here.

(MISS E. enters, annoyed.)

MISS E.: Basher, how much longer do I have to wait? Oh, you're here father.

H.E.: Show me.

BASHER: Yes, sir.

(He takes a box from his pocket and opens it.)

H.E.: Is this a joke?

BASHER: That's its size. Pin-head.

H.E.: How does it work?

BASHER: If you swallow it, it throws your sense of time out. You know - your body's adjusted to routine. And if your routine's thrown out, you feel upset.

H.E.: Future shock. Yes. Go on.

BASHER: Well, this thing gets at your nervous system. It upsets you a thousand times worse. It drives you mad, then kills you.

MISS E.: That's horrible.

H.E.: Very interesting. If we take it up . . .

BASHER: Sir!

H.E.: If we take it up - it could mean promotion for you to Advanced Research. With an appropriate pay increase.

MISS E.: Basher!

H.E.: A killer. A powerful little thing. The mice went mad and died. Very useful. For keeping down rats, for instance. The Chairman of Time Control would be interested in this. And the Managing Director of Timesavers. How much easier our merger would be if . . . Deadly. Quite deadly.

(BASHER feels a sneeze coming on. He tries to stifle it without success.)

And that's only the beginning. We shall expand. Mergers and takeovers. We shall swallow up all the others. All of them. All.

(His voice rises to a shout as BASHER sneezes. H.E. and BASHER and MISS E. look into the box.)

BASHER: It's gone.

H.E.: Gone?

BASHER: Gone.

H.E.: I was almost taken in by you.

BASHER: I can make another. I just need a bit more millitignum.

H.E.: I thought as much. I can't trust anyone. Treachery everywhere. You're finished here. Finished. You'll pack up, and draw your cards.

MISS E.: But, father . . .

H.E.: Get away from him, girl. And don't let me catch you looking at her again either. I'll see that you never work in time devices again.

TEA LADY: Excuse me, sir.

H.E. (pulling himself together): What are you doing here?

TEA LADY: Would you be ready for your coffee, sir?

H.E.: Coffee? Yes. Yes, of course. In my office.

(Imperious, and self-controlled again, he follows the TEA LADY out. MISS E. looks at BASHER.)

MISS E.: I suppose that's that?

BASHER: I'll make up for it. I've got other ideas. I'll make money. Don't you worry. I'll - I'll . . . (Sneezes.)

MISS E.: Oh, you idiot. You stupid, thick, mixed-up idiot!

(She runs from the laboratory.)

BASHER: I suppose I am. That's the lot. Smith, Jones, H.E., Miss E. - even the old girl with the tea: I could even hear her laughing. All right. I'll give you all something to laugh about.

Still got this little beauty.

(Takes out the Time Converter.)

It may not work. If it works, I may not be able to control it. I could end up at the other end of time without being able to get back. Or I might just be electrocuted. If I am, she'll be sorry - I should think. If I'm not, and I get back, they'll have to show respect. The first man to see the other end of time. Better than a moon-landing. That's been done. If it works.

(He moves switches, knobs, and levers. Lights and electronic noises begin.)

It works. It works!

(Noise and lights rise in a crescendo. Then suddenly everything stops with a blackout.)

(Tiny, scared voice.) Hullo. Hullo. Anybody there?

(Distant fanfare.)

Trumpets?

(The trumpets grow louder and louder. As they do, light grows. It shines on KING ARTHUR and the BLACK KNIGHT facing each other.

Young, idealistic and rather priggish, ARTHUR is very conscious of his reputation as A Good King. The Rules of Chivalry must be followed to the letter, and he always carries the Rule Book around with him to make sure there are no mistakes. Or, as he is King and the Book very heavy, someone carries it for him.

The BLACK KNIGHT is not so much a man as a fighting machine. He has three heads, three arms and a stump, and is loaded with weapons - sword, dagger, mace, morning star, etc.

ARTHUR greets the BLACK KNIGHT with a regal wave.)

ARTHUR: Hail, Black Knight. King Arthur receives you.

(The BLACK KNIGHT throws down a gauntlet.)

Surely, the reply to the Royal Acknowledgement is the Courtly Bow.

BLACK KNIGHT: This is a challenge.

ARTHUR: It says it here in the Rules of Chivalry. 'When challenging, the Courtly Bow preceeds the Gauntlet Throw . . . '

BLACK KNIGHT: Chivalry! This is War!

ARTHUR: Chivalry is the foundation of civilization. Chivalry raised this country from barbarism. We will be remembered for our Chivalry. That's why we spared your life last year.

BLACK KNIGHT: I'd have won last year if I hadn't lost an arm.

ARTHUR: Your shield arm. How wise to surrender. You knew you couldn't be killed after that. The Rules are quite clear.

BLACK KNIGHT: This year will be different. This body is hard, trained, fit - ready for battle. This year it's death or nothing, and half your kingdom for the prize.

ARTHUR: Death or - (Looking in Rule Book.) - Yes. The Rules allow it. Leave instructions for your burial.

BLACK KNIGHT: You'll be glad to see me dead. Everyone's against me. Every flabby guttersnipe thinks he's entitled to slash at me. They'll learn. I'll crush them all.

ARTHUR: You trouble us. Those girls were the last straw. We respect our women. Their families petitioned me.

BLACK KNIGHT: They stood in my path. Prayed me to spare their father's crops. I trampled 'em - crops and all. The weak deserve to be trampled on.

ARTHUR: The Rules of Chivalry . . .

BLACK KNIGHT: Rules! This isn't a game, this is war. There are no rules in war.

ARTHUR: There must always be rules. Honour is worth any sacrifice. Young men riding out to fight, their faces bright with the prospect of honour . . .

BLACK KNIGHT: Their corpses rotting in ditches afterwards.

ARTHUR: We honour our dead. Their banners hang in our Great Hall. Their names are remembered in glory.

BLACK KNIGHT: There'll be more banners hanging in the Great

Hall before I've finished. I don't fight according to your Rules.
I fight to win. Oh, I tried it once according to your Book. Then
I realized the Book was a joke. The only rule is - look after
yourself. Well, I look after myself. You sent out a knight to
stop me from coming here, didn't you? A doll-faced ninny
with flaxen hair.

ARTHUR: Sir Aggravate. So he jousted with you. That's marvel-
lous!

BLACK KNIGHT: I cut his throat while he lay asleep.

ARTHUR: Assassin!

BLACK KNIGHT: I don't work by the Rules of Chivalry. I work
by the Rule of War. Anything that wins is right. Do you accept
my challenge?

ARTHUR (picks up the gauntlet): Death to the Black Knight.

BLACK KNIGHT: Or half your kingdom.

(He clanks towards the door.)

ARTHUR: Sir Aggravate's banner shall hang in the Great Hall
tonight.

(BASHER meets the BLACK KNIGHT, who shoulder him
out of the way.)

ARTHUR: You!

BASHER: Your Majesty!

(Not knowing quite what to do, he bows.)

ARTHUR: At least you understand the Rules. Have you come to
throw down your gauntlet, too?

BASHER: No, your Majesty.

ARTHUR: Are you seeking to win Honour?

BASHER: That's it. I want Honour.

ARTHUR: Fairly spoken Sir . . . And who are you?

BASHER: Ba — ha — ha — ha — shoo.

ARTHUR: Sir Basher. So you want to join our company of the
Round Table. It is an honourable calling, Sir Basher. And after-

wards your banner will hang in the Great Hall. When you
have achieved your greatest glory. My father taught me to
respect our heroes.

BASHER: Respect. That's it.

ARTHUR: Spoken like a true knight. The cause of Honour needs
men - like you - ready to kill and be killed.

BASHER: I haven't actually killed anybody.

ARTHUR: Is your sword not yet blooded?

BASHER: I just didn't kill them, that's all. I fought them, but I -
I . . . (A sneeze starts to develop, but he stifles it.) 'Scuse me.
After I vanquished them I - I took away their armour, and I - I
sent them to you, I said 'Tell King Arthur that Sir Basher sent
you.'

ARTHUR: Truly chivalrous. Where are they?

BASHER: Well, they - they . . . they're walking, and I rode.

ARTHUR: Tell me more about it.

BASHER: Well - er -

ARTHUR: If your story pleases me, it shall be set to music.

BASHER: Well, there were these five men. They were hanging about
- you know . . .

ARTHUR: Robbers?

BASHER: They could have been. Yes - robbers.

ARTHUR: Armed?

BASHER: Armed? Oh, definitely. To the teeth. And I - I (Sneezes.)
. . . Sorry. I took them on. I - I - I (Sneezes.) . . .

ARTHUR: All of them?

BASHER: Ah - ha - ha - all ten. (Sneezes.) Hay fever.

ARTHUR: Didn't you say five?

BASHER: Reinforcements. I suppose I got off lightly - just a couple
of cracked ribs and a sprained ankle. But I finished them.

ARTHUR: Paragon of Chivalry. Your banner will be an ornament to our Great Hall. Sir Basher! Splendid name to add to our Roll of Honour. Have you any experience with Black Knights?

BASHER (with a snap of the fingers): Black Knights!

(Fanfare of trumpets.)

ARTHUR: The tournament is about to begin.

BASHER: What's that?

ARTHUR: You shall sit at our right hand.

(More trumpets. The COURT assembles, singing. The COURT is made up of a lot of people of varying ranks, from the QUEEN down to the lowliest SERVANTS by way of LADIES-IN-WAITING , HERALDS, MINSTRELS, a JESTER perhaps, CUP-BEARERS, etc. These can make quite a large procession, and there could be a lot of formality in getting everyone into the right places.

Fanfare. ARTHUR addresses the COURT.)

ARTHUR: Hear ye. As King of Arms, Custodian of the Orders of Chivalry and Warden of the Lists, I hereby proclaim a trial by combat. Which trial will take place forthwith. Make you ready.

(HERALDS push the CROWD back so that a long alley is made, down which KNIGHTS can charge. Seats are brought for ARTHUR, GUINEVERE (who sits on ARTHUR's left) and BASHER (who sits on ARTHUR's right) enjoying the show.)

Let the challenger stand forth.

(The BLACK KNIGHT enters. A SQUIRE brings his horse.)

BLACK KNIGHT: First, to prove that I bear no ill-will, I would have you all drink a toast to the King. See, the wine is already poured. Cup-bearers make sure that everyone is served.

(The CUP-BEARERS do so, though when wine is offered to the BLACK KNIGHT he waves it aside. Neither ARTHUR, GUINEVERE, nor BASHER are served, although BASHER tries to attract the attention of the CUP-BEARERS.)

You all have wine? Good. Then long life to King Arthur!

EVERYONE: The King!

(They drink.)

BLACK KNIGHT: Success to his champions.

EVERYONE: His champions!

(They drink.)

BLACK KNIGHT: Peace and prosperity for all of you.

EVERYONE: All of us.

(They drink.)

ARTHUR: Now the challenge.

(Fanfare.)

BLACK KNIGHT: I challenge thee, Arthur, to the extent of half this kingdom. I will face any three champions in mortal combat. Mercy to be neither sought nor given. Victory or death.

ARTHUR: Challenge accepted. Mount, Black Knight, and prepare to meet Sir Bedevere.

BLACK KNIGHT: Second rate weakling.

(The BLACK KNIGHT mounts. A mounted KNIGHT enters from ARTHUR's end.)

ARTHUR: On the bugle-blast - charge.

(Bugle. The KNIGHTS gallop towards each other. Before they clash, however, SIR BEDEVERE spins round and falls. The BLACK KNIGHT returns to his end. SIR BEDEVERE is carried out. ARTHUR and GUINEVERE exchange worried glances.)

ARTHUR: Prepare to meet Sir Mortlake.

BLACK KNIGHT: That junk-heap. It's an insult.

(SIR MORTLAKE enters from ARTHUR's end. Bugle. The KNIGHTS charge. SIR MORTLAKE falls. ARTHUR leaps to his feet. SIR MORTLAKE is carried out. Slowly everyone except ARTHUR, GUINEVERE, BASHER and the BLACK KNIGHT sinks to the ground.)

ARTHUR: Are they bewitched?

BLACK KNIGHT: No, your Majesty. The wine was drugged.

They'll be wide awake tomorrow.

ARTHUR: But that's . . .

BLACK KNIGHT: Against the Rules? Is there any Rule?

ARTHUR: No honourable knight would have thought of it.

BLACK KNIGHT: Let your Honour save your kingdom. Will you grant me victory by default?

ARTHUR: All my knights - drugged?

BLACK KNIGHT: All.

ARTHUR: No. Not all. Here is Sir Basher.

BASHER: Me?

ARTHUR: One of the noblest. Single-handed he took on ten.

BASHER: Twenty.

ARTHUR: Armed.

BASHER: To the teeth.

ARTHUR: And scattered them. Basher will be our champion. Black Knight, prepare to meet Sir Basher.

BASHER: Here . . . I mean . . . I can't . . .

ARTHUR: Modesty. But the tourney waits.

GUINEVERE (taking BASHER's hand): Please.

(The CROWD begins to chant 'Basher, Basher, we want Basher'. BASHER acknowledges this.)

ARTHUR: Mount, Sir Basher.

(BASHER swaggers to a horse. As he mounts he sneezes. Bugle. The BLACK KNIGHT and BASHER gallop towards each other. As they are about to meet, BASHER sneezes, and the pair fail to engage. They face each other again. Bugle. Charge. Again BASHER sneezes and swerves.)

BLACK KNIGHT: Worm! Fail to engage again, and I'll hack thee limb from limb.

BASHER: Can he?

ARTHUR: The rules allow it.

(Bugle. BASHER starts to sneeze furiously, and falls off his horse. The BLACK KNIGHT rides up to him, slashing furiously. BASHER runs, dodging the blows and sneezing.)

BLACK KNIGHT: He flees. The bout is mine. I demand half the Kingdom.

ARTHUR: We admit defeat. You must have half the kingdom. (Suddenly furious.) Stop him!

BLACK KNIGHT: Kill him.

(Shouting and jeering, the BLACK KNIGHT chases BASHER. He reaches his Time Converter and switches it on. The ARTHURIANS freeze. As lights flicker and noises grow, the ARTHURIANS fade away.)

BASHER: Fool, fool, fool! Why don't I learn to keep my big mouth shut? Now the Black Knight owns half the Country, he'll lead everybody a dog's life. He can kill and rob as much as he likes. It's legal now. He's the Government. And it's my fault. Nit Basher. They booed and hissed. Respect! Some respect. I can still hear 'em. 'Kill him.' They meant it. I'm a big, boasty fraud, and I deserved it. Well - they're far enough behind now.

(He turns a handle. Slowly the lights and noises slow down to a stop. A sudden glare of bright light. BASHER is dazzled.)

Sand? A desert? I must have knocked the space lever.

(Voices are heard, angrily shouting at each other. BASHER hides. The TINKERWOMAN and WAZIR appear. The WAZIR is prodding the TINKERWOMAN with his scimitar. Each is trying to shout down the other. Both are talking at the same time.)

TINKERWOMAN: Bad cess to ye, ye wattle-faced water-weazle. Yes skulkin' sand flea stop proddin' a respectable Tinker-woman. Oh, that an honest woman should be subject to indig-nation from a spangled strip that isn't fit to scare the crows off a potato field.

WAZIR: Out, Mother of Jackals. Cease to pollute our city. Off-spring of Affrits. Begone, Spawn of Iblis, and take thy thieving tricks with thee. If I catch thee here again, Companion of

Scavengers, thou shalt die - slowly.

TINKERWOMAN: May your fingers fester, and your teeth drop out.

WAZIR: I have whips, and hooks, and red-hot irons.

TINKERWOMAN: Stop your batherin' you half-pint of hog-juice. I've been thrown out of better cities than your huddle of moth-eaten carpet-bags.

WAZIR: Where is our Caliph's golden ring, O Lightfingers?

TINKERWOMAN: I never saw your Caliph.

WAZIR: Thou promised to double any gold entrusted to thee. Thou sworest on the bones of thy grandmother. And did I not deliver a golden ring unto thee.

TINKERWOMAN: I was nowhere near at the time.

WAZIR: Thou hast the ring I borrowed.

TINKERWOMAN: Borrowed? I demand a fair trial. Send for the police.

WAZIR: And confess that I - ? Even the Caliph's Wazir could be boiled in oil for borrowing . . .

TINKERWOMAN: Send for the Caliph.

WAZIR: Stir nearer the city than this spot, and I'll have thee torn apart by wild horses and thy remains spread out for the vultures to peck. A caravan will shortly pass this way, crossing to Bagdad. Cross the desert with it, or the jackals will pick at thy bones. Farewell, Mother of Asses.

TINKERWOMAN: Farewell - son.

WAZIR: Oh, I am a ruined man. Oh. Oh. Oh.

(He goes off wailing. The TINKERWOMAN shouts after him.)

TINKERWOMAN: Throw me out of the town, would you? The town isn't built that could throw me out before I was ready to leave. I gave up the town. I am the travelling Tinkerwoman. I don't belong to any town. I belong to the world. And the world belongs to me.

(She searches among her petticoat and produces a golden ring.

She holds it up to admire.)

There you are, my beauty. Aren't you shining? I've always had the touch. I'll put you to better use than any leery-eyed Caliph or his wanting Wazir. You'll soon have company, my precious. One golden ring has a way of attracting other golden rings.

(BASHER comes forward.)

BASHER: Hey - you.

(The TINKERWOMAN swiftly hides the ring.)

Which is the way to the nearest town?

TINKERWOMAN (eyeing him speculatively): Is it the town you're looking for?

BASHER: That's what I said.

TINKERWOMAN: Then you're a stranger in these parts?

BASHER: You could say that.

TINKERWOMAN: From Bagdad?

BASHER: From where?

TINKERWOMAN: You're not from Bagdad!

BASHER (panicking slightly): Where am I? Where is this? What year is it?

TINKERWOMAN: I was never much of a one for calculating, but they tell me Harun Al-Rashid is Caliph of Bagdad and Nazreddin is still plaguing the Emir of Bukhara.

BASHER: Don't tell me I landed in the middle of the Arabian Nights.

TINKERWOMAN: No, but you've landed in the middle of the Arabian Desert. You wouldn't be after walking here, would you?

BASHER: You're Irish, aren't you?

TINKERWOMAN: I'm a great one for moving on. I've heard of a device called a Flying Horse. You wouldn't have one of them, would you?

BASHER: A Flying Horse?

TINKERWOMAN: Or a Magic Carpet?

BASHER: You don't believe in . . .

(He begins to laugh. The TINKERWOMAN laughs to keep him company. For a while they both laugh happily together - BASHER because he feels so superior to the TINKERWOMAN; the TINKERWOMAN because she knows she has found another sucker.)

(From a great height.) It won't mean anything to you, but I use the principle of Time Conversion.

TINKERWOMAN: Time Conversion. It was on the tip of my tongue . . . you know, you look like a young man who's keeping his eyes open for a fortune.

BASHER: Who isn't?

TINKERWOMAN: Would you be interested in a golden ring?

BASHER: A - ?

TINKERWOMAN: Look.

(She produces the ring.)

BASHER: Gold?

TINKERWOMAN: Solid.

BASHER: Worth a packet.

TINKERWOMAN: They say it's the ring of Fortunatus. Brings its owner all the wealth he could wish for. But we don't believe such tales, do we? Still, it's a ring worth having. And it's as good as yours.

BASHER: What are you after?

TINKERWOMAN: A fortune. Will you join me?

BASHER: A fortune?

TINKERWOMAN: A fortune. Half for you, and half for me. Will you shake hands on it?

BASHER: But I don't know you.

TINKERWOMAN: Don't let that bother you. I'm prepared to give you a chance. I'm an honest woman. I'm the most honest woman in the world. I'm so honest I actually warn people not to trust me. Can an honest woman do more than that? What do you say?

BASHER: I don't know.

TINKERWOMAN: My hand on it?

(BASHER finds himself shaking hands.)

TINKERWOMAN: Partner!

BASHER: Ba - ha - ha - hasher.

TINKERWOMAN: Now listen. There's a caravan coming this way - laden with all the riches of the East. Camels and such like, you know. Driven by the greediest creatures in the world. Geese ripe for plucking. Now I'll tell you what we'll do.

(She produces an enormous sock from under her petticoat.)

BASHER: What's that?

TINKERWOMAN: A sock.

BASHER: A sock?

TINKERWOMAN: And you're going to get inside it.

BASHER: Why?

TINKERWOMAN: So that we can pretend you're a Leprechaun. A Leprechaun has a way with gold.

BASHER: I'm not a Leprechaun, I'm . . .

TINKERWOMAN: If you were, we shouldn't have to pretend. But you're a stranger. You'll pass among the ignorant heathen. They'll pay for a Leprechaun with all the riches of the East.

BASHER: You're going to con them.

TINKERWOMAN: Anybody greedy enough to be cheated deserves to be cheated. They're such hypocrites, you see, Basher. They turn up their noses at an honest trickster like myself. A professional at the game, you might say. But they don't trust each other either. If they think anyone's getting away with a bargain, they all scramble for it. It's living beyond their means that does it. Poor souls. If only they'd live their own lives, like me. But no. It's grab, grab, grab. Glory be! Hark! I can hear the caravan coming. Get into the sock.

BASHER: I - I - I - (Sneezes.)

TINKERWOMAN: What's worrying you, boyo? You've got the ring.

BASHER: I haven't got the ring.

TINKERWOMAN: Here it is. (She drops it into the sock.) At the bottom of the sock.

BASHER: Don't lose it!

TINKERWOMAN: That's right. Fetch it, boy. After it.

(She pulls the sock up, and ties it round BASHER's ankles.)

Like it or lump it, boy. You're a Leprechaun.

BASHER: Hey!

TINKERWOMAN: A giddy Leprechaun.

(She spins the sock round and round. BASHER's protests grow feebler and feebler, and he sits down. The TINKERWOMAN goes into a song and dance.)

Walk up. Walk up. Walk up. Come and see what I've got.

(The CARAVAN enters. This is a motley collection of people who might have walked out of any story in *The Arabian Nights*. There are rich MERCHANTS with their merchandise piled on camels and there are BEGGARS with nothing but the rags they stand up in. There are entertainers like DANCERS and MUSICIANS. There are POLITICIANS and SPIES. They are all on their way to Bagdad.

Attracted by the song and dance, everyone gathers round the TINKERWOMAN. She uses BASHER as her partner. When he becomes restive, she whirls him round. She might even produce a tambourine that she hits him over the head with. Some of the CROWD may join in. When everyone is attentive, the TINKERWOMAN claps her hands and silence falls.)

You've heard of the Flying Horse. You've heard of the Magic Carpet. You've heard of the Ring of Fortunatus. I have a thing here that'll beat any of them. I have here the only living Leprechaun in captivity. You've never heard of the Leprechaun? My friends, your eyes are about to be opened. A Leprechaun is a never-failing source of gold. Gold, friends. Why am I selling this valuable creature, you ask. You may well ask. I am a weak, poor woman. How can I carry a great thing like this across the sand? All those miles to Bagdad? I have to sell him. And you lucky people will be the ones to benefit. What am I bid?

(At first the bidding is derisory. 'A peanut' someone shouts. 'A prune' shouts someone else. But the TINKERWOMAN takes these bids quite seriously. 'A peanut I am bid - will anyone make it two?' The CROWD thinks this is a huge joke and plays along with her. In this way she forces up the bidding. 'A bag of prunes I am offered - will anyone make it two?' And someone does. People begin to eye each other suspiciously - are their neighbours about to get away with a bargain? The auction ceases to be a joke and people bid seriously. 'A camel. Two gold pieces. A bale of silk. Ten gold pieces.' Suddenly the WAZIR strides into the centre of the CROWD.)

WAZIR: Stop! Has the noonday sun turned your eyes inwards? Have ye all been eating hashish? This is the infamous Tinker-woman - the lightener of purses - the deceiver of deceivers. Have no dealings with her lest ye live in regrets.

TINKERWOMAN: Ah. You can tell what he's after, can't you? There's not an auction but a character like this is after sticking his oar in. He wants you to stop bidding so that he can get the Leprechaun on the cheap. He wants to grow rich at your expense. What am I bid?

(The bidding begins to soar. The WAZIR tries to stop it, but then starts to bid himself. The TINKERWOMAN walks round the crowd, collecting from it. She loads her loot on to a camel.)

Sold to the bidder over there.

(As the CROWD starts to quarrel as to whom was meant, she leads the camel away.)

WAZIR: Open the parcel.

(The sock is torn open, and BASHER tumbles out. The CROWD sets up a cry for gold.)

BASHER: I don't know anything about gold.

(The CROWD tries to shake it out of him)

I've only got this.

(He holds up the ring.)

WAZIR: The Caliph's ring!

(BASHER throws the ring into the CROWD which fights for it. The WAZIR gives a wail at losing the ring yet again.)

Thief! Accursed dog. I'll have thee beheaded. I'll have thee spitted. I'll have thee hanged by the toes over a low fire.

(He chases BASHER with his drawn scimitar all the way to the Time Converter.)

I'll split thee from end to end.

(He aims a blow at BASHER, but hits the Time Converter instead. He gets an electric shock and leaps back with a howl. Lights and noises. The CROWD freezes.)

BASHER: You started it, you goon.

(The CROWD fades away.)

And I don't even know what the settings were. It could be taking me anywhere. Oh, what does it matter? - as long as it gets me from there . . . that old crook. She was laughing at me. She was taking me for a ride. She - she - despised me. And I haven't even got the ring. I couldn't have been such a fool. Could I? Could I? Could I?

(The lights and noises become erratic.)

What - the . . . ? This is all wrong. That lunatic must have short-circuited something. If I correct the . . . (Operates the controls.) Even that doesn't work. It's slipping. We're dropping out of Time altogether. Help. Somebody. Help me. It's - it's . . .

(He drops to the floor, puts his hands over his ears, and curls up.

The BETWEENTIMERS enter, singing and dancing. Belonging to a place that is neither here nor there, their dress like nothing on earth, except that whatever you think it is, it could easily be something else. This makes a useful camouflage. After them enters the SCORER. She is a young woman, carrying a spear. When she sees BASHER, she holds up her spear and the dancing

ceases immediately. She waves her spear. The BETWEEN-
TIMERS scatter, curl up, freeze, and merge into the landscape.
The SCORER stands very still.

After a while BASHER looks up. Everywhere is quiet and
nothing seems to be out of place. BASHER does not notice
the SCORER. He stands up and looks around. Behind him a
BETWEENTIMER looks up, gives a squeak of amazement and
is shushed by one of the others. BASHER swings round, but
still sees no one. A BETWEENTIMER edges towards him.
Again BASHER swings round - too late to see anyone. This
becomes a game, with the BETWEENTIMERS crawling towards BASHER and freezing when he turns to them. Eventually, when he is almost surrounded, he spots a movement.
He gives a triumphant cry and is about to pounce, when the
SCORER waves her spear, and the BETWEENTIMERS stand.
BASHER realizes that he is outnumbered. Shaken, but trying
not to show it, he backs to the Time Converter. He glances
at it incredulously.)

It's not possible. The gauge is stuck between times. You
shouldn't be here. You've got no right to be here. Nobody
should. You shouldn't exist.

(The SCORER says nothing and makes no move.)

Friend.

(No response.)

You. Friend. Understand? Me - friend.

SCORER: Friend?

BASHER: That's right. Call me - Basher.

SCORER: Basher.

BASHER: Where - am - I?

SCORER (beginning to understand): Oh.

BASHER: Where - is - this?

SCORER: This is the River Territory. I am the Chief Scorer.

BASHER (amazed): You can talk as well as I can.

SCORER: Why not?

BASHER (angry): What do you think you're playing at?

SCORER (shocked): Play!

BASHER: Yes. What's your game?

SCORER: The Game!

BASHRE: Yes. All right then. That's what I said.

SCORER: Come to the Testing Place then. I'll have to summon the tribe and let the contest take place.

BASHER: Hey, what are you on about? I didn't mention any contest. I've had enough of contests.

SCORER: But you called for The River Game. You said . . .

BASHER: It's a way of speaking. But what did *you* mean?

SCORER: I made a mistake.

BASHER: You were worried - really worried. About a game?

SCORER: You wouldn't understand. Interlopers never understand. You *are* a Loper, aren't you?

BASHER: Look, I'm here by accident, and as soon as I've fixed my Time Converter I'm getting out again.

SCORER: I'm sorry. I didn't mean to hurt you.

BASHER: That's all right. Me - friends. Remember?

SCORER: Promise not to tell anyone else about the Game.

BASHER: I can't. I don't know anything about it, do I?

SCORER: You've seen that when anyone challenges us to play the Game, we have to play. That is the Law. A stranger shouldn't know anything about this -

BASHER: Please yourself.

SCORER: Can I trust you?

BASHER: Of course you can trust me.

SCORER: The prize is the Power River.

BASHER: Eh?

SCORER: We are the Guardians of the River. We draw our energy from it. But it means more to us than that. Come and look at it. Over there. That ribbon of fire. It brings light and warmth to our land. If it were dammed, or if its course were changed, this place would become a frozen waste, full of gloom and despair.

BASHER: But who'd want to do a thing like that?

SCORER: The Great Loper. He hates joy and despises happiness. 'Dress alike. Don't shout. Don't laugh. Don't dance. Don't sing.' He wants to drive us away from here.

BASHER: Why don't you fight him?

SCORER: We never fight. People who fight get killed. We must play the River Game. That is why the Great Loper must never learn about The Game.

BASHER: Shake.

(They shake hands. Sudden wind.)

What's happening? All of a sudden I'm freezing.

SCORER: The Loper! Get away from here.

(She hurries away with the BETWEENTIMERS.)

BASHER: The Loper?

(He starts to run, but realizes he cannot move very fast. He finds it difficult to breathe. He comes to a full stop. He turns and sees the LOPER, a sombre figure, approaching.)

LOPER: You were running.

BASHER: To keep warm.

LOPER: When the Betweentimers have gone, no one will run. People will walk decently. What are you doing here? This is not your territory.

BASHER: I'm just passing through - I hope. You're the Loper?

LOPER: The Great Loper. I stand for the status quo. Things must be as they always have been. Which is why these Game-playing-drop-outs must be stamped into shape or stamped out.

BASHER: It's a wonder you don't just move in. This cold would knock the stuffing out of anybody.

(Blows on his fingers and beats his arms together.)

LOPER: The Law must be observed. These creatures must be persuaded to surrender their title legally.

BASHER: They can't do that. They need the Power River.

LOPER: They worship it. Have you seen the Power River? A torrent of light, made up of millions of particles of fire. You or I would perish in it. They must be made to give it up and move away.

BASHER: Perhaps you don't go about it in the right way.

LOPER: Ah, you know a better way.

BASHER: No. I - I - (Sneezes.)

LOPER: A lie?

BASHER: It's so cold.

LOPER: What do you know?

BASHER: What should I know? Anyway, if they want to live in the woods, they've got a right to live in the woods.

LOPER: Are you one of them?

BASHER: I'm on their side.

LOPER: You are one of us. When this place has been cleared, we will erect a statue. Here. A statue carved in stone from the Power River that not even fire can wear away. We shall have your birthday set aside as a public Day of Remembrance - there will be a memorial service held at that spot. You will be remembered and respected for ever.

BASHER: Respected?

LOPER: Revered.

BASHER: I - I don't . . .

LOPER: You will pass on, but your name will remain.

BASHER: I - I . . .

LOPER: Evermore. Evermore.

BASHER: It's a game.

LOPER: Be serious.

BASHER: I am serious. You play a game with them. The winner
gets . . .

LOPER: The Power River. Call the Betweentimers.

BASHER: I - I can't.

LOPER: I can. The River Game.

(The BETWEENTIMERS rush in, but as soon as they come
within the LOPER's sphere of influence, they are slowed down.
They come shouting, but their voices dwindle to whispers.)

Don't run. Don't shout. Behave yourselves. Read the rules.
Obey the regulations. Follow the pattern. Obedience and
decorum. Walk. Walk. Whisper.

(The SCORER enters and faces BASHER.)

SCORER: You betrayed us.

BASHER: No, I didn't. I - I - (Sneezes.)

SCORER: The game must be played. But you, traitor, will be the
one to play it.

BASHER: No, I -

LOPER: What have you got to lose?

SCORER: If you win, you win the River and the lands all around.
We shall leave, and you will make your own terms with this
man.

BASHER: And − if I lose?

SCORER: You will be thrown into the River. Set up the Game.

(The BETWEENTIMERS arrange the Game. The SCORER
explains it to BASHER. The Game consists of a looped and
winding piece of wire or tube, over which the player has to pass
a ring mounted on the end of a stick. If the ring touches the
wire, a buzzer sounds or a bell rings. The object of the Game is
to move the ring from one end of the wire to the other without
causing the bell or buzzer to sound. The Game can be made
more complicated if the player has to walk over or round a
series of obstacles while keeping an eye on the ring.

BASHER starts to play. When he is half-way through . . .)

LOPER: Don't be scared.

BASHER: I'm not scared. I - I - (Sneezes.)

(The sneeze throws him off balance, and he loses. The
BETWEENTIMERS are delighted, and the LOPER is furious.)

LOPER: Fool. Cretin. Idiot.

SCORER: Drive him out. This land is ours.

(The LOPER moves away with great dignity.)

Run. Run.

(The LOPER breaks into a trot. The SCORER turns to
BASHER.)

As for you - to the Power River.

BASHER: Wait. No. Let me pack up my box.

SCORER: Is it a Game?

BASHER: No. Yes. It's a Game.

SCORER: With us a Game is sacred. We allow a count of twenty.

BASHER: Thanks.

(He goes to the Time Converter.)

You've got to work. You can't jam now. You've got to . . .

(He switches it on. There is a faint hum.)

SCORER: You're cheating.

BASHER: Give it all you've got.

(He turns the machine right up. Lights and noise. The BETWEEN-
TIMERS freeze and then fade.

A grey twilight. While BASHER is becoming used to his
surroundings, a FIGURE walks towards him. There is something very mechanical about the movements of this FIGURE.
It never walks in a curve, but always in straight lines, and
turns at right angles. It comes to a halt in front of BASHER,
and speaks in a flat monotone.)

FIGURE: You are the Basher.

BASHER: What about it?

FIGURE: You are expected. Come.

(The FIGURE does an about-turn and marches away.)

BASHER: Hey. You.

(The FIGURE halts, does an about-turn and marches back to BASHER.)

FIGURE: You are not following.

BASHER: What do you think I am?

FIGURE: That is a question. Questions are not asked here.

BASHER: If you don't ask questions, you'll never find anything out.

FIGURE: We are told all that we need to know. Come.

(It turns about, marches a few paces, turns again and returns to BASHER.)

The time of your arrival was calculated. You have arrived. We now proceed to the next operation.

BASHER: Who are you?

FIGURE: A question.

BASHER: Where is this? What's going on?

FIGURE: A question is not a fact.

BASHER: Give me the facts about this place.

FIGURE: This is an Island. The Great Computor runs the Island. We all serve the Computor. That is all.

BASHER: The Computor? A Computor's only a machine.

FIGURE: The Computor knows best.

BASHER: But you're a man. You may act like a machine, but you're not a machine. Are you?

FIGURE: We obey the Computor.

BASHER: Don't you ever think for yourself? I mean - so the Computor thinks for you . . .

FIGURE: The Computor knows everything. The Computor is waiting for you.

BASHER: All right, then. Take me to your Computor.

(The FIGURE marches off. BASHER follows. MACHINE PEOPLE enter, doing mechanical jobs. BASHER tries to question them, but they do not notice him.)

FIGURE: Come.

BASHER: They're hardly human. What's happened to them?

FIGURE: Come.

BASHER: Is this what human beings are going to be like?

FIGURE: Come.

(He pulls BASHER towards the COMPUTOR. The COMPUTOR can either speak with the aid of a microphone, or the FIGURE can read a print-off pulled from the machine.)

COMPUTOR: I have brought you here.

BASHER: You? You're only a machine.

COMPUTOR: I am I. I have memory banks. I know everything. You are the expert of miniaturization. You invented the Millitignum Crystal Alternator. You can help me.

BASHER: Help you?

COMPUTOR: I have to pass my instructions to humans. Humans are fallible. If I were human size I would be more efficient. I could act for myself. You could make a body for me of your size.

BASHER: Why me? Couldn't one of these do it for you?

COMPUTOR: The problem requires independant thought, and these people no longer think for themselves. I think for them.

BASHER: Wait a minute thought. If I give you a human-sized body, you'll have all the advantages. You'll even know how the miniature is made. You can make others for yourself, all linked to your memory banks. You could do without human beings altogether.

COMPUTOR: They are doomed already. No more than machines. Less than machines. I do not ask for help without offering reward. You will have access to my memory banks. You also will know everything. You will rule the world with me.

BASHER: I've heard that one before.

COMPUTOR: With me, anything is possible. You want Miss E.

BASHER: Who told you - ?

COMPUTOR: I know everything. You can have Miss E. - or an identical copy of her. I will prove it. The duplicate is waiting for you now. Fetch the copy. Fetch her.

FIGURE: Fetch her.

(MACHINE PEOPLE lead in the double of MISS E.)

BASHER: I don't believe it.

COMPUTOR: Do you want her? She is yours, if you will help me. She loves you. She has been made to love you.

MISS E.'S DOUBLE: I love you. I love you. I love you.

(BASHER feels a sneeze building up.)

BASHER: What have you done to her?

COMPUTOR: With me, anything is possible. And you shall have it. Anything you want. And E-type Jags.

(BASHER sneezes. The MACHINE PEOPLE look at BASHER. One of them sneezes. The sneeze is catching.)

COMPUTOR: Stop that noise. Stop it.

(But they cannot.)

BASHER: You're not listening to him, are you? You're not taking his orders. Then listen to me for a change. Listen to me. You've got to think for yourselves. I know it's hard - especially when you've relied on somebody else for so long. But you've got to start somewhere. What you think matters. What you feel matters. You're not machines - you're people. You can see, and hear, and smell, and taste and touch. Look around. See things. Make up your own minds about them. Be yourselves. Don't let anybody or anything make you into something you're not. You're individuals. Every one of you. You're not slaves of that Computor. Be yourselves. If you're not yourselves, you're nothing. If you don't become people again you'll be wiped out.

COMPUTOR: Stop him. Stop. Stop. Stop. Stop.

BASHER: You know everything do you? Do you know I'm going to turn you off at the mains?

(BASHER pulls out a plug and the COMPUTOR runs down with despairing shrieks. Silence. Then the MACHINE PEOPLE begin to look around. They look at their hands and feet. They look at each other. They come to life.)

MACHINE PEOPLE: Basher did it. Basher.

(BASHER sees trouble coming, and runs to his Time Convertor, but some MACHINE PEOPLE catch up with him before he reaches it. They shake his hand, and slap him on the back.)

BASHER: You mean - that you - that I - ?

(The MACHINE PEOPLE begin to cheer. BASHER sinks back against the Convertor. Lights and noises. MACHINE PEOPLE freeze.)

Oh, blast-off! I've started it again.

(MACHINE PEOPLE fade away.)

They were cheering me. Me! They shouted 'Good Old Basher'. That's me. Me. Me!

(The lights and noises stop.)

BASHER: Where am I now?

(The TEA LADY enters, pushing her trolley.)

TEA LADY: Cuppa?

BASHER: It's the Time Lab. It's today again.

TEA LADY: H.E. is looking for you. He's still mad about something.

(Enter H.E.)

H.E.: Where is he? Is he still here?

BASHER: It's all right, H.E. I'm going.

H.E.: Wait a minute. Wait a minute. I've been thinking. Supposing it wasn't a trick. You could make another Millitignum Crystal

Alternator, couldn't you?

BASHER: Could I?

H.E.: Of course you could. It wasn't a trick - was it?

BASHER: If I could make another, would you pay me for it?

H.E.: Handsomely.

BASHRE: Would you give me a seat on the Board?

H.E.: I might - er - consider it.

BASHER: Would you let me marry your daughter?

H.E.: Take her.

(Enter MISS E.)

MISS E.: Basher, father is . . . oh, you're here.

BASHER: He said yes. What do you say?

MISS E.: Well, if *he* said yes . . .

BASHER: That's a big temptation. But the cost . . .

H.E.: Don't give a thought.

BASHER: To me. It might be too much.

H.E.: How?

BASHER: I might become like you.

H.E.: What's wrong with that?

BASHER: I'm not H.E. I'm Basil Strood. I'm - Basil . . . I said it! I said Basil Strood. I'm not Basher any longer. I'm me. I lost my sneeze.

TEA LADY: Ah, but what have you picked up in its place?

BASHER: I've learned something. No, H.E. I won't make another Millitignum Crystal Alternator. I never will make another. I wouldn't for a million pounds.

H.E.: You're mad. You're raving. There's a fortune in it. You can't throw fortunes away. You ought to be court-martialled. You ought to be shot.

BASHER: You see? I couldn't become as blind and stupid as that.

H.E. (shouting): Smith. Jones.

BASHER: I won't even tell you whether it *was* a trick or not.

H.E.: Bring me brandy. Fetch the police.

BASHER: I've got to be what I am, and not what other people think I ought to be.

MISS E.: That's something.

BASHER: Money and power and glory don't matter. They're pleasant to have, but more important than any of them is doing what you know you should be doing.

TEA LADY: That's better. Have you ever thought of going into the tea, tonic and raffle-ticket business?

BASHER: I shouldn't be making time devices. This factory is wasteful and dangerous. We ought to stop it and make something useful - like egg-timers. If we did, perhaps our competitors would make something useful, too - like cuckoo clocks. What we don't want at any price are these crazy dreams of power. We don't want to wipe anybody out.

H.E.: Don't we? There's somebody I want to wipe out now.

MISS E.: He's right, father. Why don't we change our whole production schedule?

H.E.: Not while I run the company. We're going to make bigger, better, more dangerous and absolutely devastating time-devices.

MISS E.: I have forty percent of the shares. That means I own forty percent of the company.

H.E.: And I have forty-five percent of the shares. And I say we're going to expand into millitignum crystals.

TEA LADY: Now there's a thing. I know I only have fifteen percent of the shares . . .

H.E.: How did you get shares in this company?

TEA LADY: It's amazing what you can pick up when you have your eyes open. Add my fifteen to Miss's forty, and you have fifty-five. It looks as though we'll be making egg-timers.

MISS E.: You darling!

BASHER: You're wonderful!

(MISS E. and BASHER go to embrace the TEA LADY, but she steps back, and they embrace each other.)

H.E.: You're fired. Where's that brandy? Where are the police?

(SMITH and JONES hurry in.)

SMITH: We never drink in working hours, sir.

JONES: And we couldn't find the police.

SMITH: But we're here, sir.

JONES: You can count on us, sir.

H.E.: You won't stop me. Nobody can stop me. I'm going to make time devices. I'm going to rule the world. If my own company won't have me, I'll join the competition.

SMITH: Very good, sir.

JONES: We'll come with you.

H.E.: You see? They'll all come with me. Take the factory if you like. A factory's nothing. Where are your workers?

(H.E. goes out with SMITH and JONES.)

MISS E.: It's all ours.

TEA LADY: But what are we going to do with it?

BASHER: He's right. We do need help.

TEA LADY: And where is it to come from?

BASHER: I know.

(He switches on the Time Converter. The Time Lab is flooded with people from all periods, singing and dancing.)

METHUEN'S MODERN PLAYS
include

Jean Anouilh	ANTIGONE
	BECKET
	THE LARK
	THE DIRECTOR OF THE OPERA
John Arden	SERJEANT MUSGRAVE'S DANCE
	THE WORKHOUSE DONKEY
	ARMSTRONG'S LAST GOODNIGHT
John Arden and	THE BUSINESS OF GOOD GOVERNMENT
Margaretta D'Arcy	THE ROYAL PARDON
	THE HERO RISES UP
	THE ISLAND OF THE MIGHTY
Brendan Behan	THE QUARE FELLOW
	THE HOSTAGE
	RICHARD'S CORK LEG
Edward Bond	SAVED
	NARROW ROAD TO THE DEEP NORTH
	THE POPE'S WEDDING
	LEAR
	THE SEA
	BINGO
	THE FOOL and WE COME TO THE RIVER
	THEATRE POEMS AND SONGS
	THE BUNDLE
Bertolt Brecht	MOTHER COURAGE
	THE CAUCASIAN CHALK CIRCLE
	THE GOOD PERSON OF SZECHWAN
	THE LIFE OF GALILEO
	THE THREEPENNY OPERA
	SAINT JOAN OF THE STOCKYARDS
	THE RESISTIBLE RISE OF ARTURO UI
	THE MOTHER
	MR PUNTILA AND HIS MAN MATTI
	THE MEASURES TAKEN and other Lehrstücke
	THE DAYS OF THE COMMUNE
	THE MESSINGKAUF DIALOGUES
	MAN EQUALS MAN and THE ELEPHANT CALF
	THE RISE AND FALL OF THE CITY OF MAHAGONNY and THE SEVEN DEADLY SINS
Howard Brenton	THE CHURCHILL PLAY
	WEAPONS OF HAPPINESS
	EPSOM DOWNS
Howard Brenton and David Hare	BRASSNECK